★

LAIKA

NICK ABADZIS

COLOR BY Hilary Sycamore

:01

First Second
New York & London

5.50

CHAPTER 1

I have a better chance if I keep the coat and just keep walking.

If I give you my coat, I'll still die of cold when you let me off in Magadan.

As I see it, you've got no choice. Anyway, you'll be *warm* in *here.*

Please ... I *need* my coat. Without it, I'll freeze to death.

Give me your coat and I'll take you.

I – I have no money.

What can you pay me?

All right.

Please ... I need to get to Magadan.

Thank you! Thank you!

Easy, friend. That's a bad cough.

KOFF
KOFF
HAAACK*
KOFF

KOFF

I know.

For most, there's only **one** way out of the Kolyma gulags.

Lucky.

KOFF

I've been recalled to Moscow. My case is being reinvestigated.

Korolev.

KOFF

What's your name, friend, and why are they letting you walk out of the gulag?

Deal. Let's go.

What about this sweater? It's old but thick and warm.

All right, you've got a point. What else have you got?

And you won't get the coat.

No. If you do that, you'll **definitely** die.

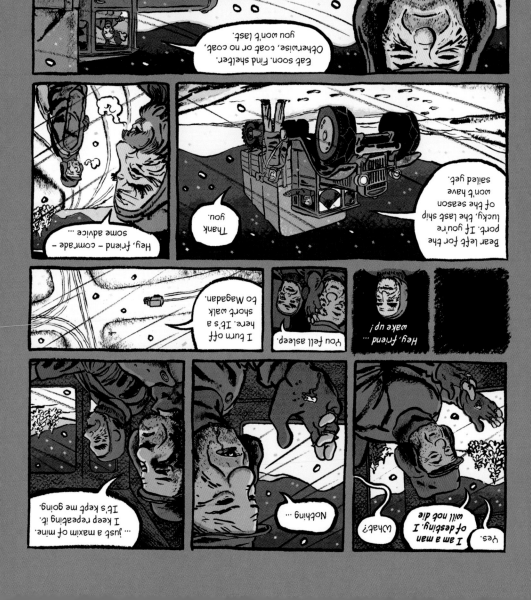

Sorry ... comrade.

For God's sake, comrade, come in and shut the door. You're letting in a draft!

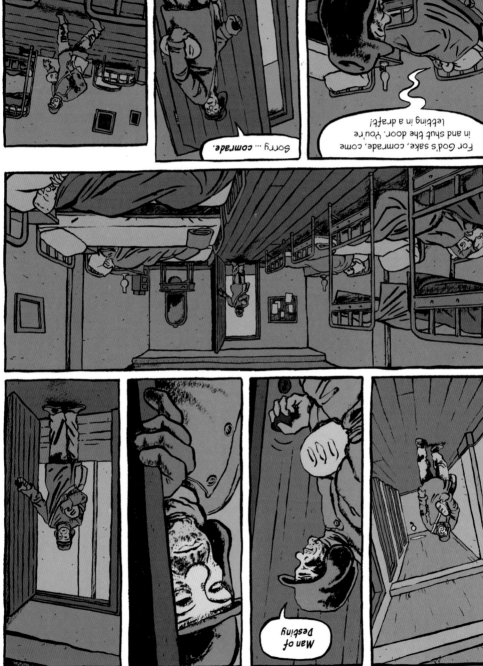

Man of Destiny

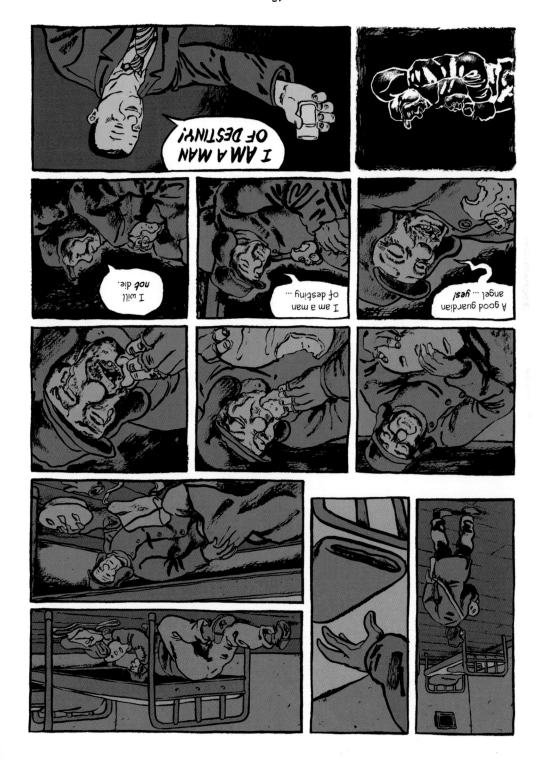

And to *you*, my friend … I've not forgotten *you*.

Shabarov! Extra rations to celebrate. Dispense one teapot each of extra alcohol to every man on this launch ground!

Immediately, Chief Designer!

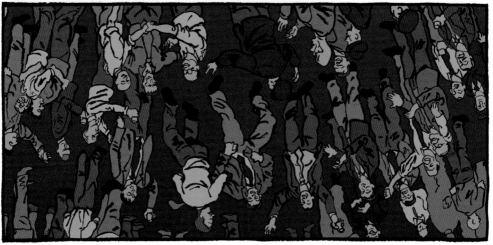

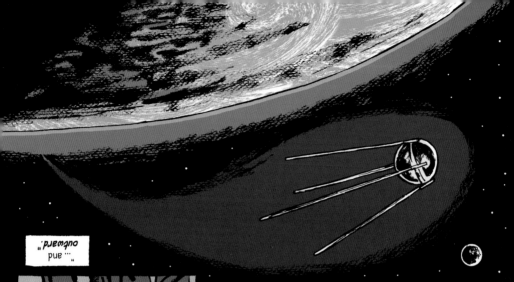

As soon as possible.

The Council of Chief Designers is meeting with Khruschev's aide tomorrow ...

... But the Premier wants to speak with you today, in private.

Excellent! I *knew* he'd get it!

Driver, drop these two back at the bureau and then take me straight to the Premier's office.

Yessir.

He's all revved up, Antonina.

Comrade Mishin ...

Is it really *true* that Chief Designer Korolev was once a prisoner in a gulag?

Yes, it's true. Because of *false allegations*, of course. He never speaks of it and neither should *you*.

He loves his country, like any other Russian.

I didn't mean – I just meant to say, how *remarkable* –

I know.

Ready yourself, because I have a feeling it's not going to stop here.

Comrade Korolev! This *is* a remarkable achievement.

Oh, I laughed when I thought of all those yankees tuning in their radios to hear the *beep-beep* of our Sputnik ...

So ingenious.

Thank you, Premier.

But what I want to know is, how soon can you launch *another* one?

Another ... ?

This is only the first step to realizing our *dream* – putting Russians on the Moon!

A *month!* Maybe it can be done ...

That's the spirit. It's a *challenge!*

Now recall Chertok and the others. We have work to do.

OKB-1 is the best design and engineering bureau in Russia. Imagine the kudos *another* launch will bring us!

We *can* do this.

We *must.*

Yesterday, it launched Sputnik I !

"True ...

CHAPTER 2

Get rid of them!

It's hardly fitting for the home of a high-ranking government official, is it?

This is intolerable, Tatiana. A disaster!

Three years earlier

MOSCOW

Mama, can we keep Kudryavka? You *said* she was special!

Sigh

No. We already have a dog and a cat.

I have too many mouths to feed as it is, Tatiana. Why would I want another?

Take my advice and dump them.

Throw them in the river.

A *puppy?* God, *no!*

He already feeds all the filthy strays as it is!

Only one or two ...!

We don't need any more dogs!

All right. I understand.

Bleeding-heart *madwoman.*

What are you looking at? Get back to work!

NOBODY LOVES ME! WHY SHOULD I LOVE THE DOG?!

Shame on you, Mikhail Korovin, for treating that puppy the way you do. She's a special dog. All she needs is a little love and affection.

¡GO ON!

Don't you get it? I don't *want* you. Get lost!

...Still here?

RRUF?

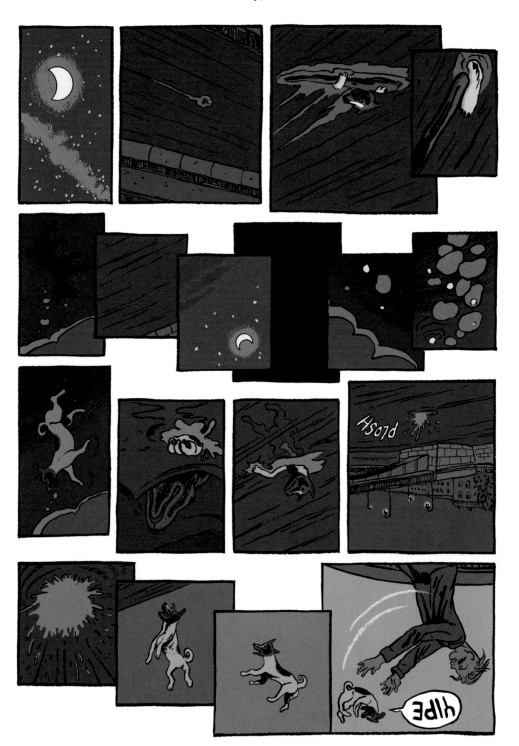

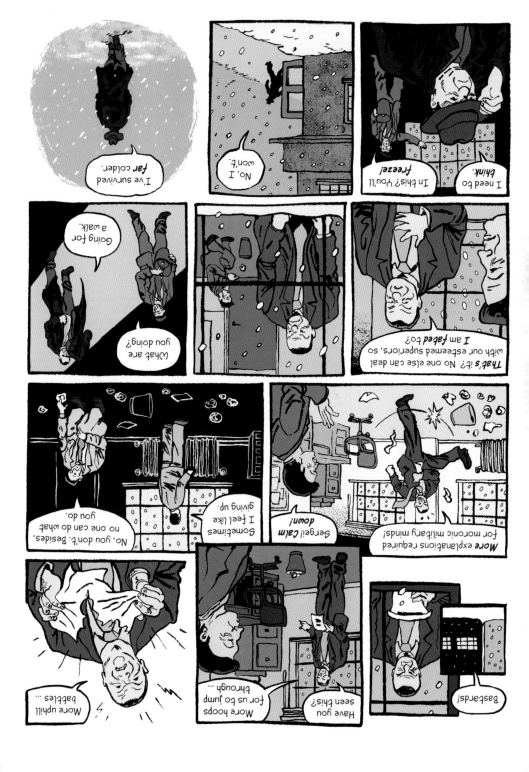

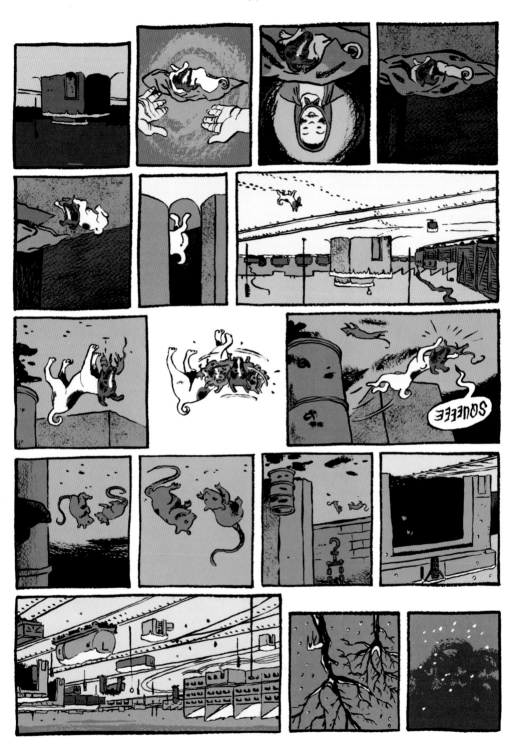

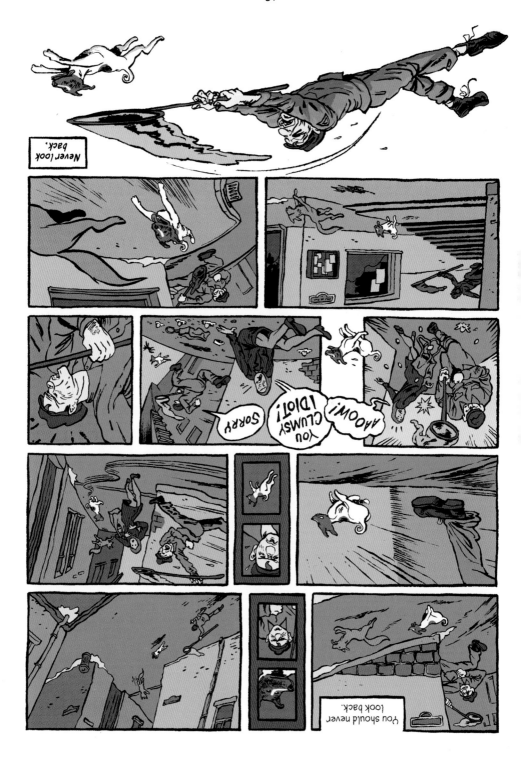

Never look back.

Although, those you leave behind ...

... will still think of you.

WOF! WOF!

RUF! RUF!

New friends, new family ...

Don't worry.

WUF?

ROF!

Filthy mutts.

... YYYHHHOOO

AAAOOW!

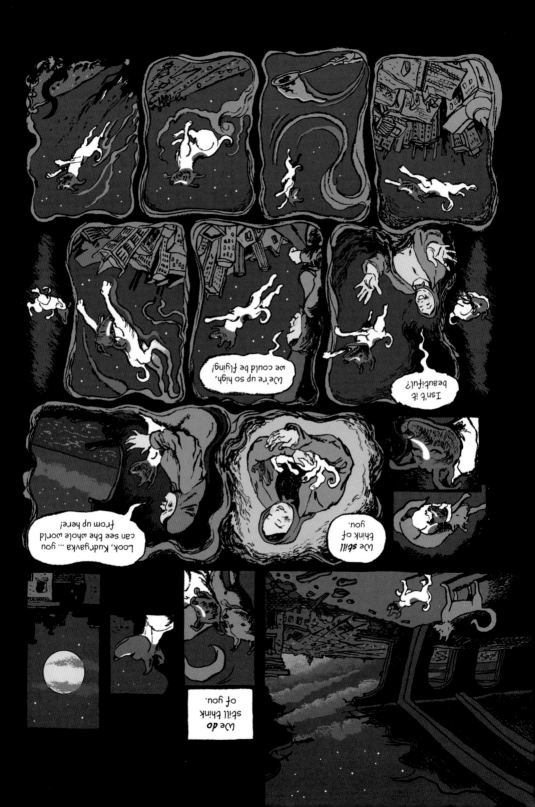

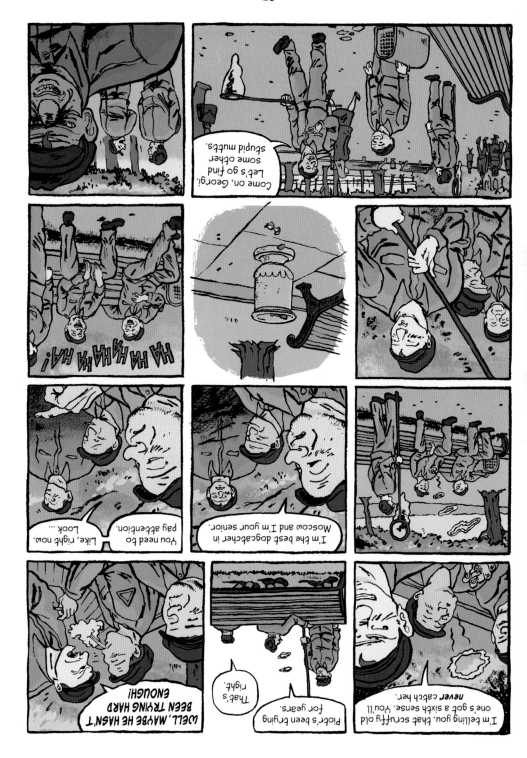

Sergei ... are you all right?

What?

Oh, yes.

We're **safe** for a little while, Vasili Pavlovich.

We're no longer **mavericks**.

For a little while.

59

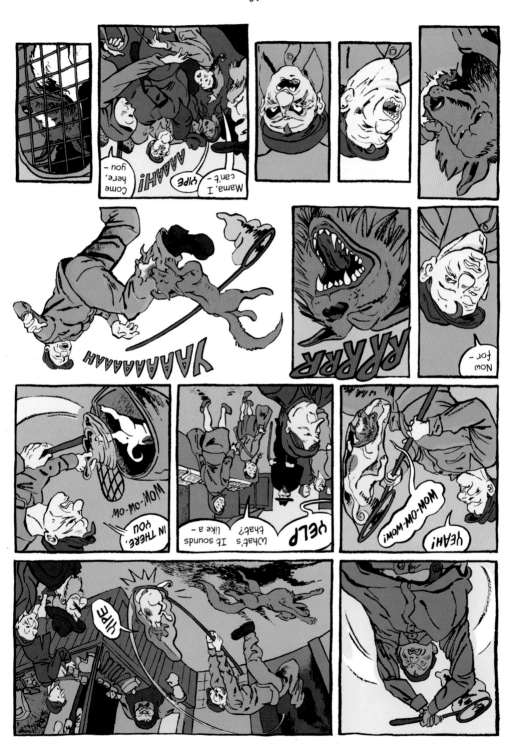

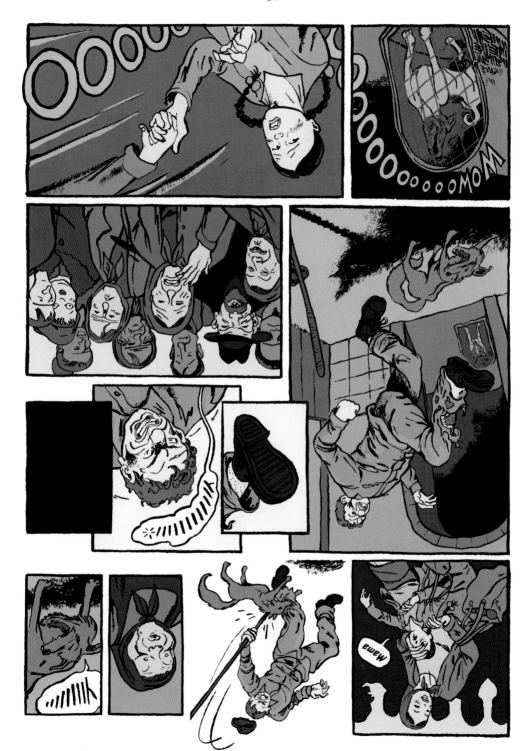

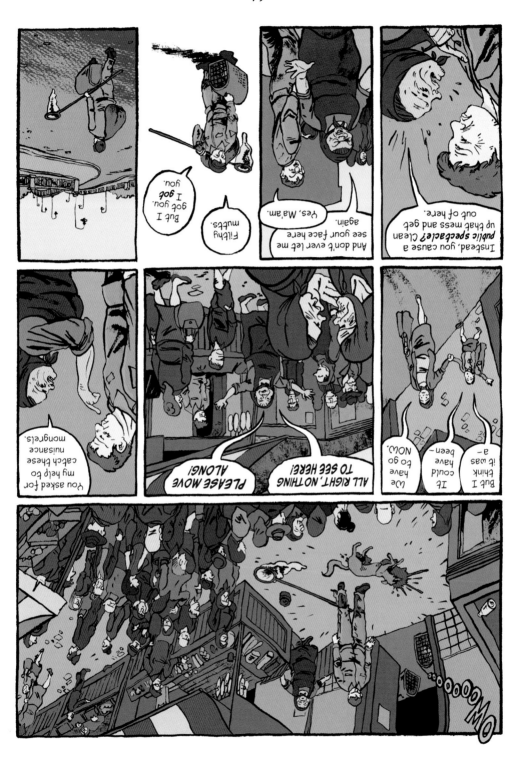

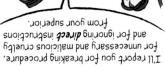

CHAPTER 3

Moscow, Summer, 1956

The Institute of
Aviation Medicine:
IMBP

My, my …

Well, hello!

Come on, girl!

Psst … Zhuchka!

The dogcatcher called her Zhuchka.

Oh?

Makes for more easily maintained sanitation equipment in confined spaces on, uh, *special test flights.*

All our dogs are female.

Her name. It's a *she.*

What's his name?

Please! Come on, let's have a look at you.

May I …?

Hm. Bit shy.

Our newest recruit.

I think she might've found the canine confinement capsule a bit disconcerting at first ...

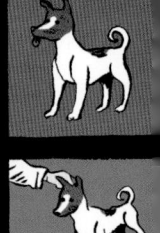

But once I explained that it was to get the dogs used to the tiny spaces they inhabit aboard test flights, she understood.

Good.

Dr. Gazenko's been showing her the ropes. Ah, there he is now.

Oleg Georgivitch, have you looked in on Yelena today?

On my way there, now. It's Kudryavka's first day at the centrifuge...

...might be a bit overwhelming for both of them.

Care to join us?

I have a meeting, but keep me updated.

Indeed.

Oh, and Oleg ...?

The latest test-flight at Kasputin Yar was successful. The Chief Designer is personally returning both test subjects to us this afternoon.

I'll be ready.

Indeed.

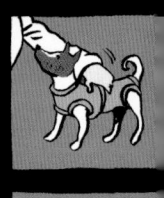

Indeed.

But whatever I can give, I'll be *proud* to serve my country and the communist party.

I've made all my oaths and declarations, Dr. Gazenko.

I'm sure everyone's been a little *evasive* with you, mentioning *test flights* and all sorts of technical terms, without explaining what they really mean by them.

What I am about to tell you is a *state secret.*

... there are a few things you need to know.

But if you're to take care of these little canine souls properly ...

... difficult.

I believe you've already met Doctors Buylov ...

Popov,

Seryapin

and Parin ...?

... Doctors.

Gentlemen ...

... our newest subject for training – *Kudryavka*.

What is this machine?

A centrifuge. It simulates the g-forces a dog would feel upon rocket launch.

?

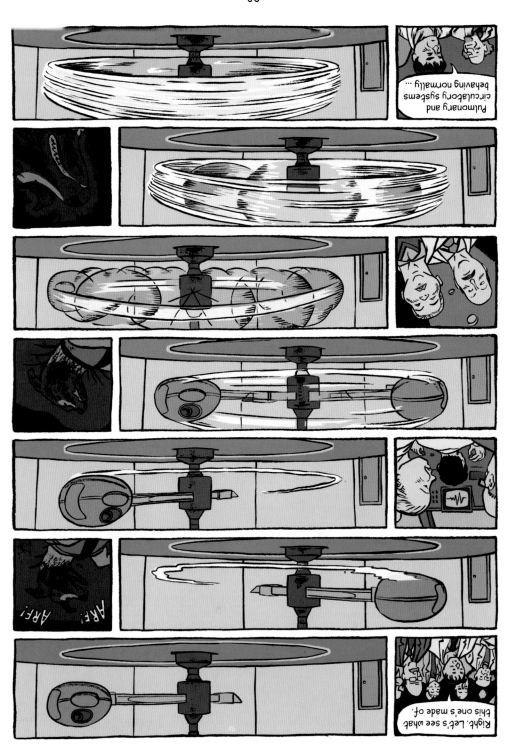

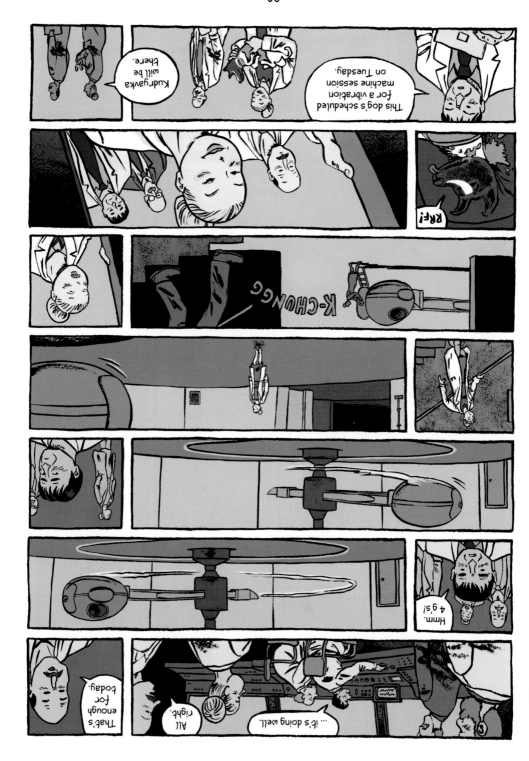

Well, she's regained her appetite.

Soon we'll have to wean her off meat scraps and onto gel food.

Gel food?

Yes. the idea is, gel is easier to eat up in space.

So, you begin to see ... our work here is a lot to get used to.

I'm *up* to it.

It's fantastic. Rocket flights...

It'll take a little while to *grasp* it all.

Where is Dr. Yazdovsky?

Ah, Chief Designer. How nice to see you.

I need to debrief Yazdovsky. He isn't in his office.

He's in a meeting. I'll find him for you.

Hello!

I'm Boris!

Uh, hello!

Right. Thanks.

84

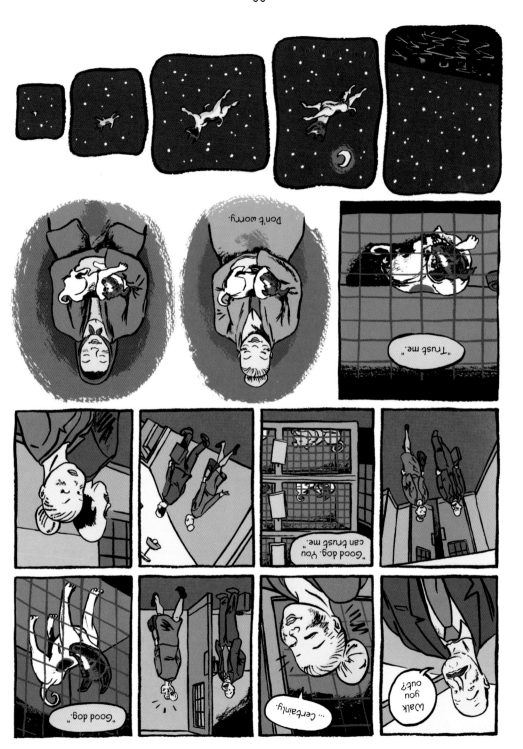

Zhukovsky Air Force Base,
35km outside Moscow

October, 1956

Whose idea was this, again?

The physiological data this test will yield will be invaluable.

So it was *your* idea.

It was *Yazdovsky's*.

He's always keen to introduce the latest training methods.

Don't worry, Yelena ...

The dog cabin is padded and pressurized. All Kudryavka will experience is a little confusion and maybe some nausea.

Nausea?

She's used to that – she's been through it all ...

89

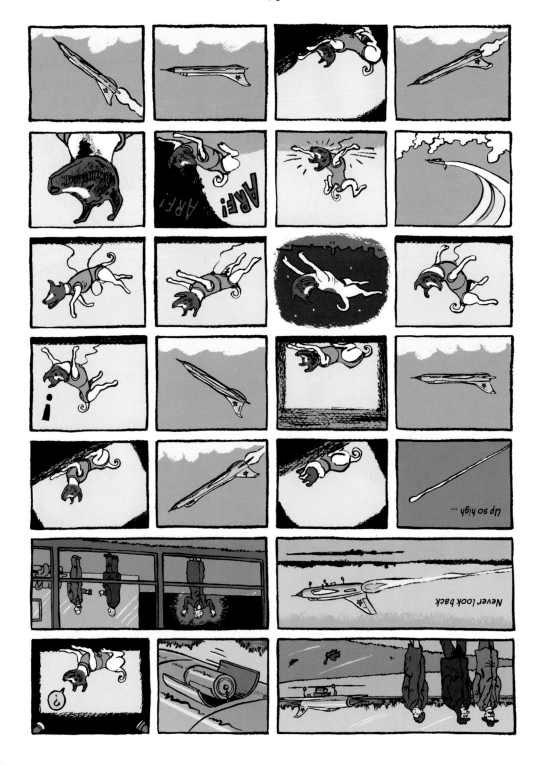

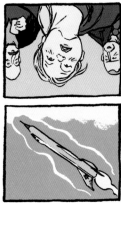

What *did* Blagonravov say?

Tell you another time!

Let's collect the data.

Yes, of course.

Psssst!

Exactly as Academician Blagonravov warned, eh, Vladimir Ivanovitch?

Don't get too fond of the dogs, will you, Yelena?

... No, Doctor.

Yes, well...

She's always happy to see Yelena, Vladimir. Especially after a training session.

ARF! ARF! ARF!

I've never seen this dog so so animated. Isn't she normally quite placid?

YIP!

WAKE UP!

Good dog...

Are you all right?

Kudryavka?

Unusual. Her first reaction seems to be *enjoyment* ...

...before confusion, or fear.

She *was* enjoying it! At least, at first.

Fascinating! But why?

No idea. We could send up more dogs and compare results.

There are plans for that.

From a physiological standpoint, I'd say these test results were very positive.

Once again, Kudryavka proves that she's got incredible endurance for a small dog.

Extraordinary ...

Yazdovsky was having trouble interpreting Kudryavka's reactions to zero G.

Really?

He couldn't figure out why she appeared to be enjoying it – at least, early on.

Well, maybe it was like being stuck on one of the rides in Gorky Park for too long.

Ha!

It follows ...

Anyone would get ill and hate it if they stayed on an amusement park ride as long as that.

It's easy to see why she was pleased when it stopped.

You really are becoming a behavioral expert on these dogs.

Thank you. I can usually tell what's bothering them.

That still doesn't really explain her reactions. She's a *dog!*

What can I tell you? Dogs have emotions. Besides, she's a special dog.

Indeed ...

Members of the Space Medicine Group ...

I'm not at liberty to discuss specifics, but the Chief Designer at the OKB-1 rocket plant tells me that 1957 will see more of his projects in development.

General Staff Meeting ...

January, 1957

So, we must be ready. Lt. Col. Yazdovsky...?

Thank you, Academician Blagonravov.

Intensive animal training will continue ...

We have built a new engine vibration simulation chamber ... each dog will undergo sessions in this ...

Comrade Dubrovsky will, as ever, be in charge of dog-handling ...

That's one of the reasons we train them – so they'll cope better.

Actually, seeing Blagonravov today reminded me that you once mentioned a story about him ...?

Oh, that ...

That would be about Tsygan.

Tsygan? A gypsy?

Indeed. And we passed that point a long way back.

Come on, Yelena ... why so glum? We live in exciting times, we have exciting work ...

I know ...

But when I heard about the new engine simulation chamber I began thinking about what the dogs will have to go through.

I'm sure you had something to do with it.

Oh, I make my observations but Yazdovsky forms his own opinions. He was showing how much he trusts you.

Dr. Yazdovsky trusted me to do a good job from day one.

As I recall, it was you who had to be won over!

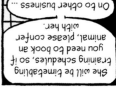

On to other business ...

She will be timetabling training schedules, so if you need to book an animal, please confer with her.

So, the first thing on Yazdovsky's list was recognition of **Comrade Dubrovsky** in front of **Boss Blagonravov** and the whole department! A **commendation**.

I suppose so.

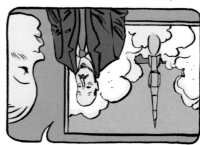

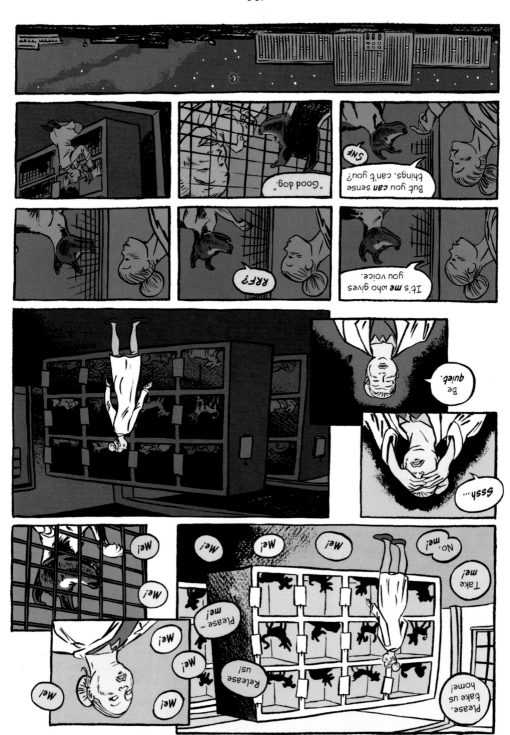

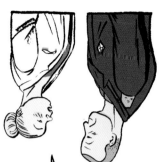
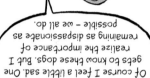

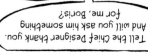

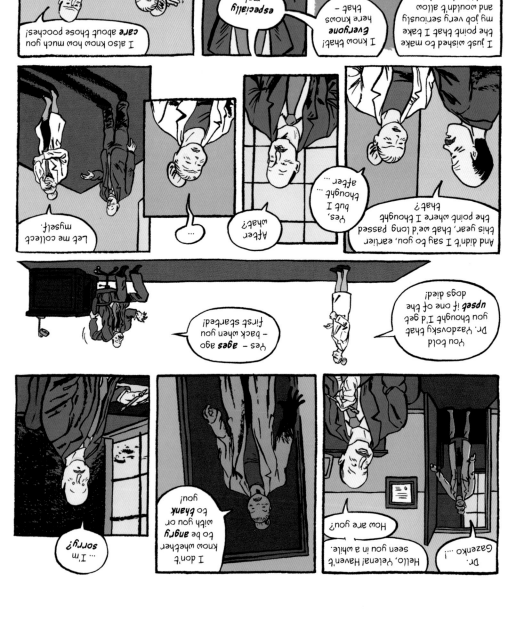

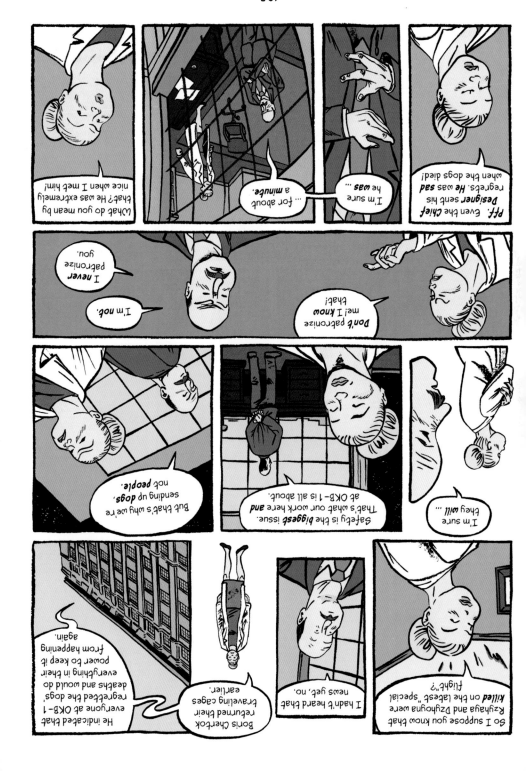

OKB-1 Rocket Design Bureau,
Monday June 3rd, 1957

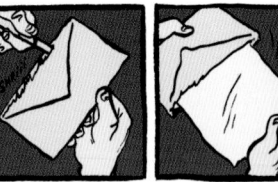

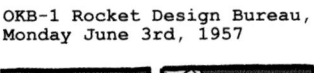

Главный Военный Поверенный

From: the office of USSR
Chief Military Procurator

Re:
Sergei Pavlovich Korolev

Meeting of the Military
Collegium of the USSR
Supreme Court,
April 18th 1957

All remaining charges
against the above-named
have been summarily
dismissed, due to the
lack of any crimes.

Николай АБАНИС

Chief Military Procurator

I am not a *prisoner* any more.

I AM A MAN OF DESTINY!

IMBP, Tuesday 27th August, 1957

ARF!

Honestly! No job is worth it if it follows you out into a lovely, sunny day like this one.

Mm. I can't think of many other reasons for such a long face! ...

... No!

Not unrequited love, then. Is it unwanted attention?

You've become so preoccupied since you've been there. Have you fallen for a colleague?

No!

... Yes.

You're thinking about work – again.

What?

Yelena, what's on your mind?

Gorky Park

Moscow, Sunday August 25th, 1957

Here we are, Cosmodogs ...

... happy landings!

Welcome home, Belka and Modnitza!

Yes, I'm pleased to see you, too!

But you've got to be patient a little while longer so that Doctors Parin and Seryapin can examine you ...

ROF!

Psst – Comrade Dubrovsky!

?

Yes, Boris?

There are no more "rocket dog" launches scheduled for about a year!

OKB–1 is busy with a host of *other* projects. *Sssh* – top *secret*.

Ha! I knew you'd be pleased.

Thanks, Boris. You're a dear man!

I try, I try!

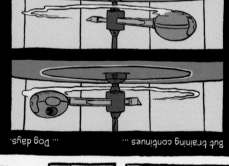

... is not to worry.

The secret ...

Most of the time, we don't notice.

Which is just how it should be.

Every day, every moment is a frontier to a country that, once crossed, can never be returned to.

One must learn not to.

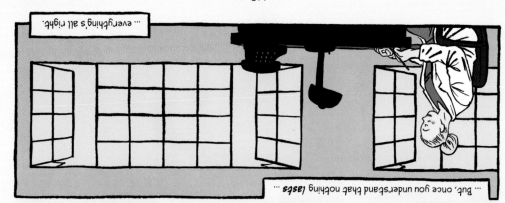

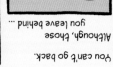

118

God's Teeth!

A MONTH?!

I know. It's a *crazy* deadline.

Crazy? It's *impossible!*

And I just sent the *whole bureau* on vacation!

Call them *back.*

Vasili, we have the *blessing* of the *Premier.*

... We must make this date "*without fail.*"

A month! Maybe it can be done.

That's the spirit! It's a challenge.

Now recall Chertok and the others.

We have work to do.

CHAPTER 4

Although I don't have any exact dates, I've been told we have a very short period of time to prepare three animal candidates for a new "special" flight.

Dr. Parin, I'm putting you in charge of selecting these three. Two of the animals will be backups.

Dr. Gazenko will oversee an intensive training schedule for each candidate.

I'll talk to Yazdovsky.

Please.

...

But whatever it is - I want to be a part of the team.

I can't talk about it.

I know. I

It's senior staff only.

Something's going on.

I'm on my way to a meeting ...

I know - one I haven't been asked to attend.

Oleg ...

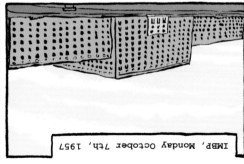

IMBP, Monday October 7th, 1957

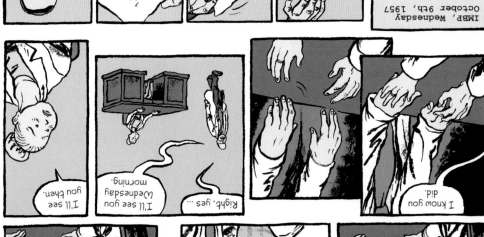

Welcome, Chief Designer!

You remember our head animal technician, Yelena Dubrovsky ...?

Good to see you again, Comrade Dubrovsky.

Vladimir tells me you're doing a fine job looking after our dogs.

I do my best, Chief Designer.

Our dogs.

Now, Comrade Parin – the dogs you've chosen?

Yes. Ahem.

Mukha ...

Albina ...

Albina! An old friend – a good dog.

... and *Kudryavka*.

Of these three dogs –

Comrade Dubrovsky, will you have those three isolated? Just to be safe.

Immediately, Chief Designer.

126

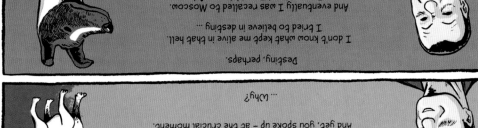
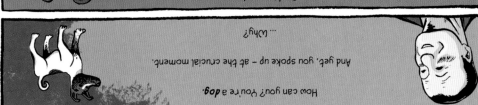
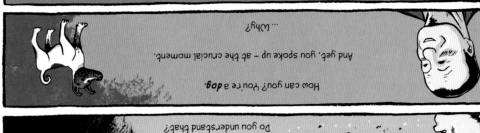

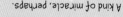

This is Laika's container.

It's smaller than I thought it would be ...

And he wants it up there as soon as possible?

Yes. We'll do it, even if we have to cut some corners.

Let's just say that the Premier has realized the propaganda value of satellite launches.

Why so tight?

There are still problems, but we'll solve them. Even on such a tight schedule!

SPUTNIK!

The first spacecraft ...

Gentlemen ... this will be Laika's vessel!

I'm sorry,
Yelena ...

I'm sorry,
Kudryavka.

Excuse me
for a moment,
gentlemen.

And I must tell you
about the radio
broadcast ...

The dogs will need to
arrive at the launch
ground on the 29th ...

Now, let's
go over
some
dates.

I only hope that the technical achievement of
Sputnik II will outweigh the sad but necessary
sacrifice of one small dog.

Indeed.

Be careful what you say, Oleg Georgivitch. I can guess what you're getting at ...

... and as your boss and your friend, I'm warning you – *keep your mouth shut.* We're not here to question *the purposes of our superiors.*

Forgive me, Vladimir. I don't know what came over me.

Driver, let Dr. Gazenko off at the next corner, please.

But all along I should've been watching you.

No.

There are people who care more for their animals than their fellow man. No – I – I'm a scientist.

But I favor *good* science.

I'm sorry, Vladimir. I was *surprised.* We have to be matter-of-fact about this. You haven't formed an attachment to this damned dog, have you?

"Damned" ... indeed!

Unbelievable! I was worried about *Yelena* going soft – we *both* were!

Don't ever put me in a position like that again.

Don't take the Chief Designer on. He's powerful – and becoming ever more so.

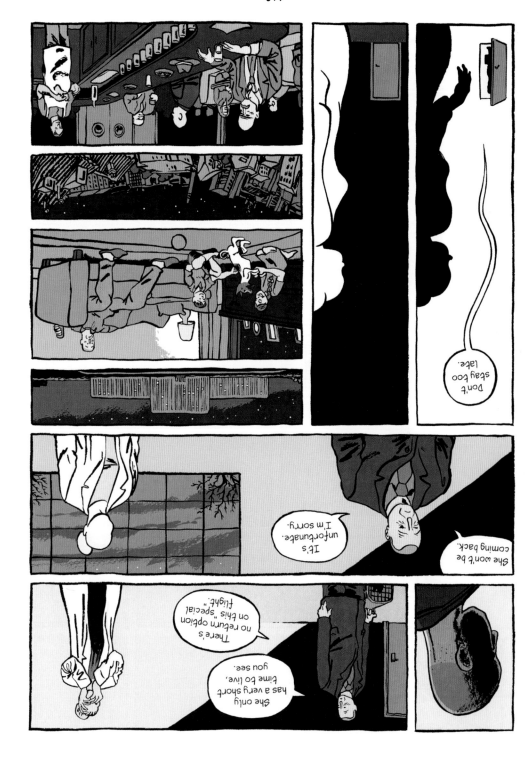

Hello.

Hello.

You look like you haven't slept.

You too.

It's all right ...

I heard.

I know what's going to happen to Kudryavka.

Where *is* she?

Yazdovsky wanted to do something nice for her ... took her home to meet his children ...

Maybe you *got* to him, Oleg Georgivitch. Maybe it was *worth* the trouble you got yourself into yesterday.

You heard?

Not exactly. Yazdovsky alluded to an exchange.

You really don't like the Chief Designer, do you?

I understand why, now.

Oleg, I'm sorry for any misunderstandings we've had.

Doesn't matter.

Funny thing ... sometimes I fool myself that there are such high ideals in my work.

But it's all a *game*. And Korolev is the grand master of it.

Oleg, it's *dangerous* to say such things ...

Not to *you.*

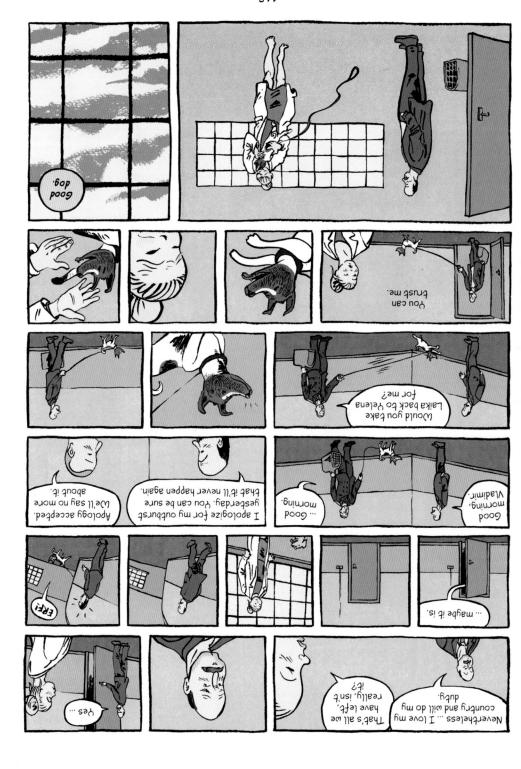

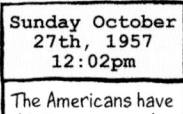
Sunday October 27th, 1957 12:02pm

The Americans have their own as-yet-unlaunched satellite, which they have named *Vanguard*.

But Soviet satellites are ahead – Soviet science is at the forefront of new technology ...

The people of the Soviet Union are building a new way of living!

The fortieth anniversary of the Revolution will be marked by the launch of a second artificial satellite.

This satellite will have a passenger – the first living creature to orbit this planet!

People of the Soviet Union, may I present to you ...

... LAIKA!

ARF!

ARF!

They're sending a dog up in a rocket?

I think that's what he means.

ARF!

ARF!

ARF!
ARF!

IMBP, Monday October 28th, 1957 09.15am

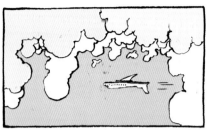

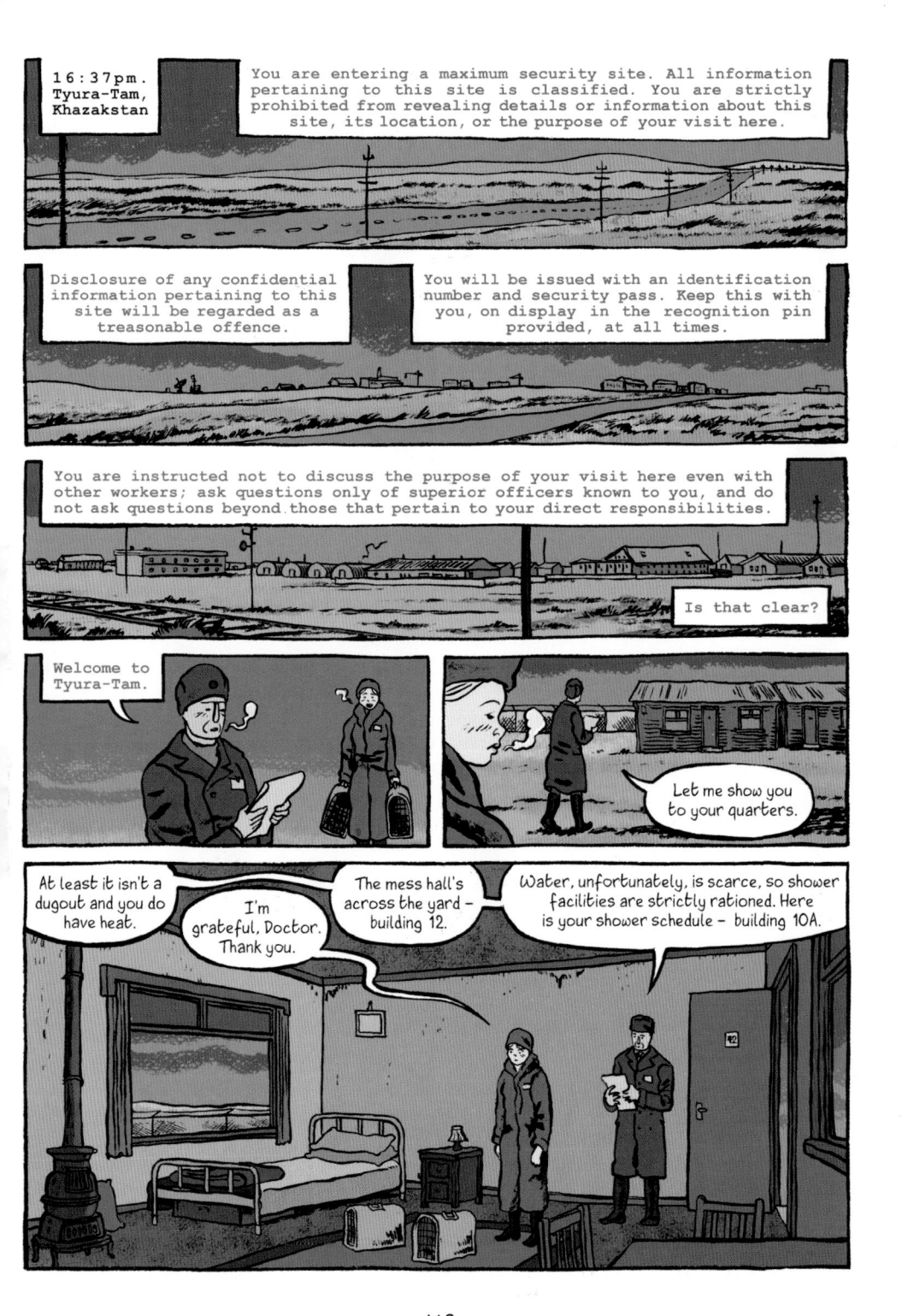

16:37pm. Tyura-Tam, Khazakstan

You are entering a maximum security site. All information pertaining to this site is classified. You are strictly prohibited from revealing details or information about this site, its location, or the purpose of your visit here.

Disclosure of any confidential information pertaining to this site will be regarded as a treasonable offence.

You will be issued with an identification number and security pass. Keep this with you, on display in the recognition pin provided, at all times.

You are instructed not to discuss the purpose of your visit here even with other workers; ask questions only of superior officers known to you, and do not ask questions beyond those that pertain to your direct responsibilities.

Is that clear?

Welcome to Tyura-Tam.

Let me show you to your quarters.

At least it isn't a dugout and you do have heat.

I'm grateful, Doctor. Thank you.

The mess hall's across the yard – building 12.

Water, unfortunately, is scarce, so shower facilities are strictly rationed. Here is your shower schedule – building 10A.

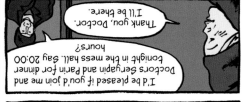

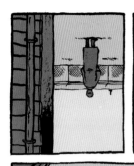

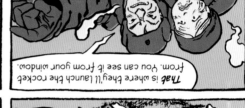

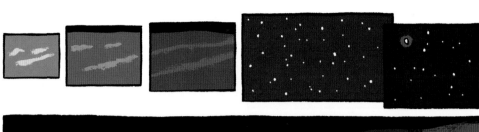

... This place is a **monument** to man's ambitions.

This place ...

Where we don't let dogs be dogs ... or even people be people.

... is a place where **we** do what we do best.

This place ...

What is this place?

How do you seem to know?

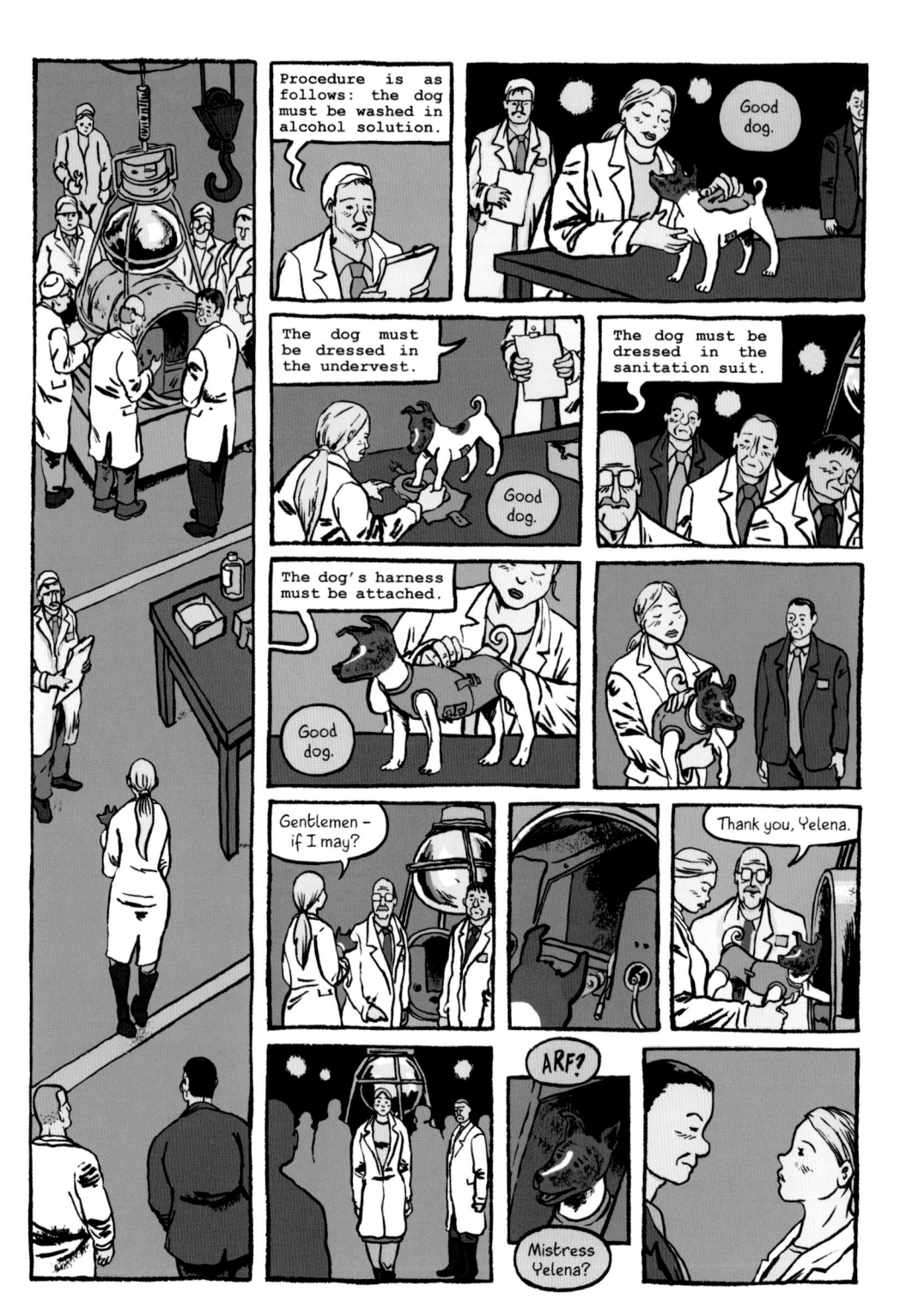

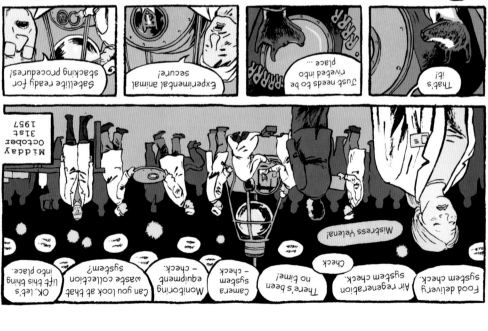

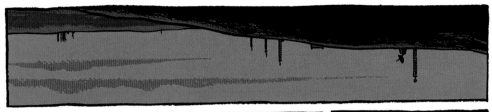

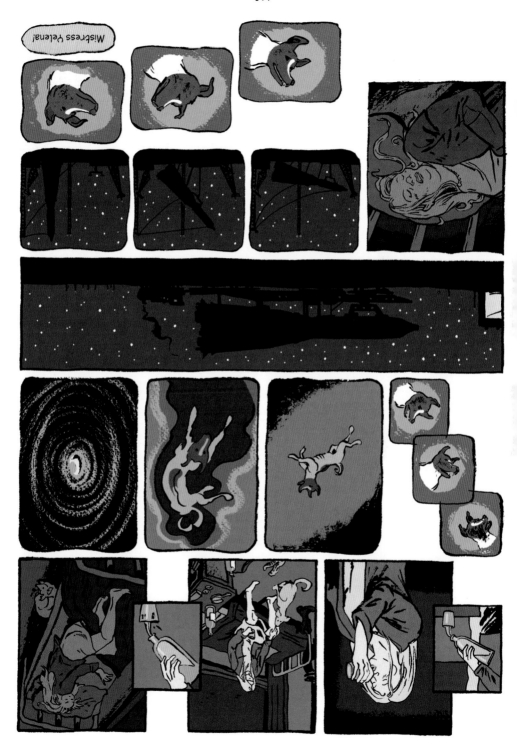

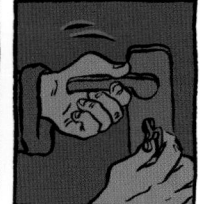

Saturday November 2nd, 1957, 00:50am

165

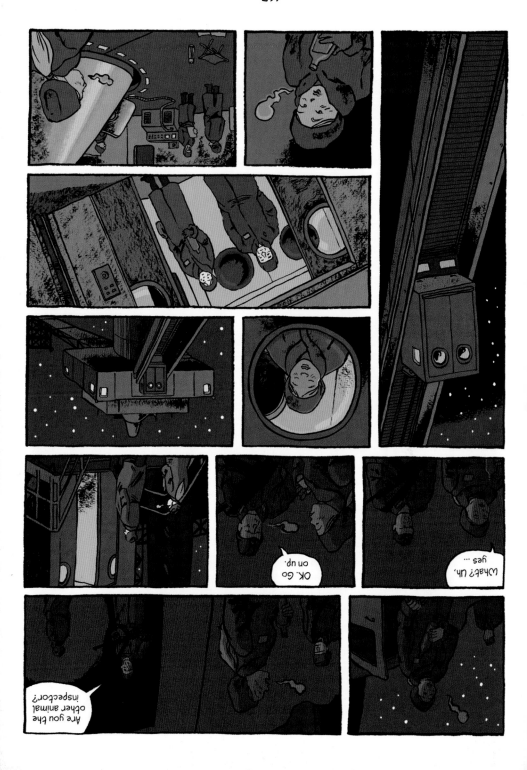

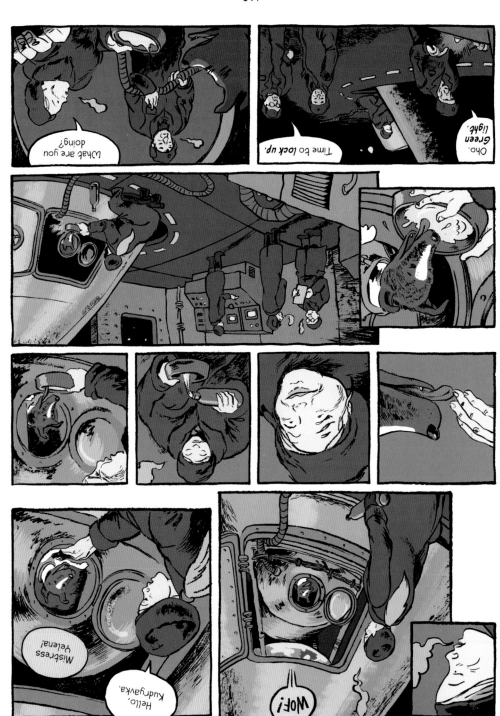

¡HAHA!

¡HAHA!

I'll say it's impressive. That dog's going to be the world's first, genuine space traveler!

... you begin to realize just what the Chief Designer has achieved.

It's incredibly impressive, isn't it? Once you see it up close – the gantry, the rocket ...

Tell the command bunker we're ready for box room retraction and final preflight checks.

Right, let's go.

CHNKK *

CLUNGG

Check?

Check. Let's get this outer hatch sealed, too.

Container hermetically sealed.

Mistress Yelena!

Bolts fixed.

RRRRRR

NOK NOK

02:52am

Yes?

Dr. Yazdovsky ...

Yes, Doctor.

Are you ready?

Thank you for allowing me to check on K – on Laika that last time. She enjoyed her drink of water.

That's all right.

02:15am

02:00am Moscow Time

Launch Day

Sunday November 3rd 1957

... 4440

Can't you take me home with you?

Let me out ...

Mistress Yelena ...

175

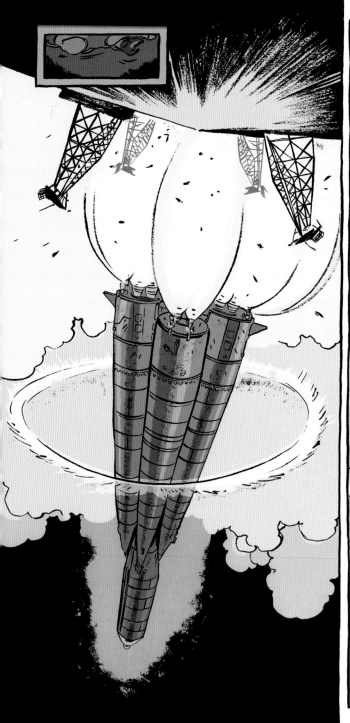

good dog?

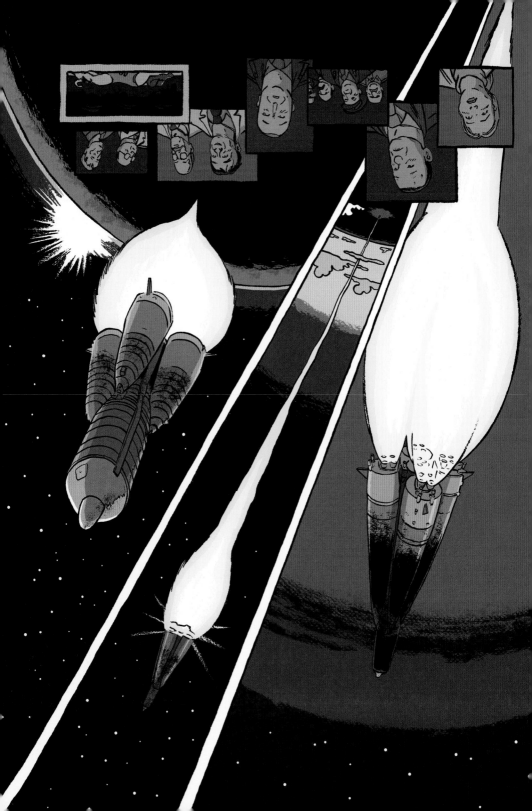

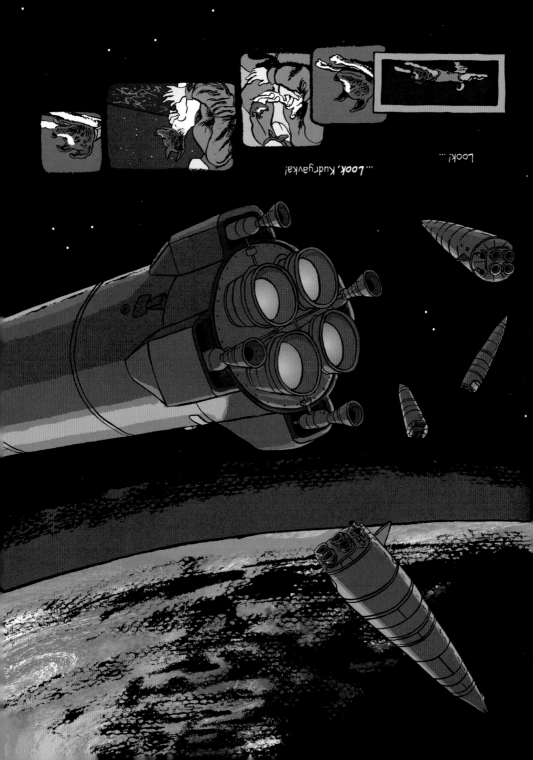

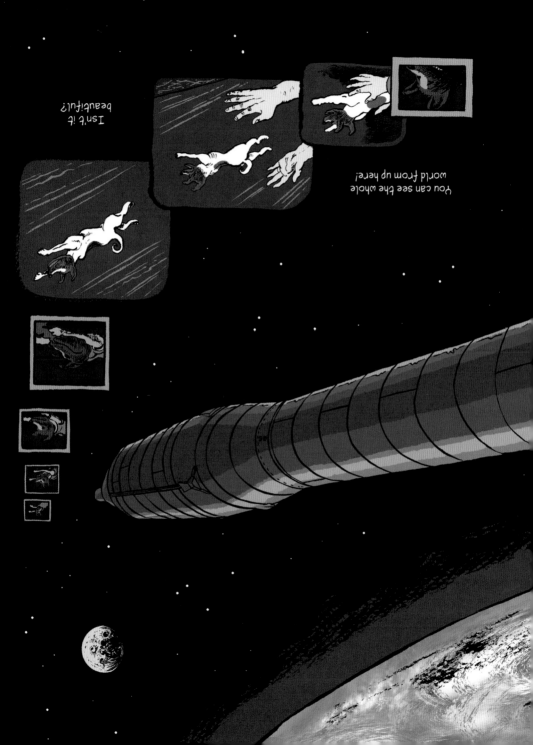

Well? Has it separated?

Unclear.

No, wait.

There seems to be a problem.

Orbit at inclination of 65.3 degrees to the equator. Velocity: 29,000 KPH.

...

Nose cone should've jettisoned.

Yes! WE'VE DONE IT!

Ha! You've seized the high ground, Laika!

Orbit insertion successful.

She should be in zero-G. now.

Nearly four times higher than prior to launch.

But, under the circumstances, vital signs are good.

Respiration?

Experimental animal's pulse has tripled.

Telemetry?

Might cause a problem with thermal control ...

Pulse rate beginning to decrease ...

But *slowly*. Only very slowly ...

She's panicking. She must be terrified.

Listen, *everyone!* Today we've made *history*.

Laika is alive! And if a dog can survive in orbit, then so can a man!

And a man will be next — you'll see!

Ryazansky, phone Moscow. Tell them ...

Tell them that Russia has successfully launched the world's first space traveler.

LAIKA!

Kudryavka.

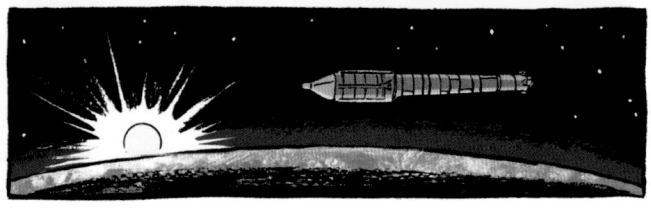

181

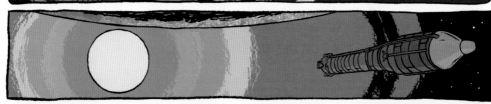

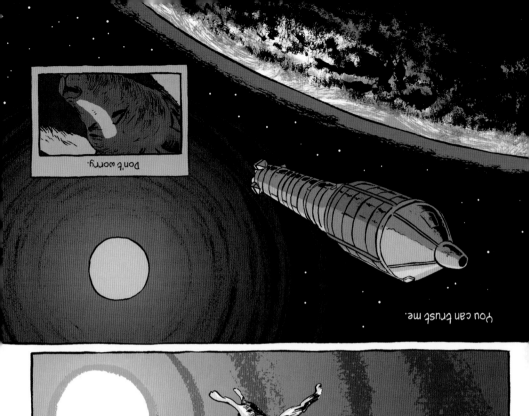

Don't worry.

You can trust me.

You can
trust me.

Don't worry ...
good dog.

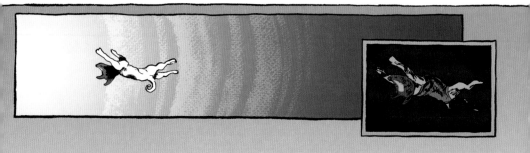

New York News
SPUTNIK II LAUNCHED
Second Artificial Satellite Carries Living Cargo: a Dog Cal...

THE LONDON TIMES
Second Soviet Satellite Launched
Dog On Board

La Planète Quotidienne
ANIMAL DANS L'ESPACE!
Comment les Soviétiques descendront-ils le chien

Die Welt Heute
Russen Schießen Zweiten Satelliten Ab
Hund ist Inner... Raumschi...

O M...
Lua... por...

人 是 聲 音

Monday November 4th, 1957

Here's a good one ..."The American press have nicknamed Laika *Muttnik*. Mutt is American for mongrel ..."

Further news on Laika the space dog in response to the questions of the world! She has caught the imagination of millions of people!

Unfortunately, Laika is not destined to return alive. She will die painlessly in space, euthanized from a lethal dose of –

Lies.

189

Panel: Vasili! Come into my office, quickly!

Antonina's putting through a call from the Premier ...

Panel: What's the matter with you, Boris?

We did something incredible. We built Sputnik II and put it up there in just *one month!*

Panel: So what? It was a *dog.* How could you have known that the Boss would convince the Premier to lob it up there?

Bah!

I told that poor girl at the kennels that there'd be no more dog launches this year.

Panel: The West seems as worried about the dog as they are about Russian superiority.

I doubt *that.*

Panel: That one's from the London *Times.*

Ha! That official makes it sound like we've got a vehicle *ready* to fake a man up!

But the world doesn't like that the dog died. It's terrible publicity!

Panel: OKB-1 Rocket Design Bureau

"In London, a Russian embassy official told outraged dog lovers that many humans had volunteered to go into space aboard Sputnik II ...

"...but a dog was sent instead as the sacrifice of a man was unacceptable."

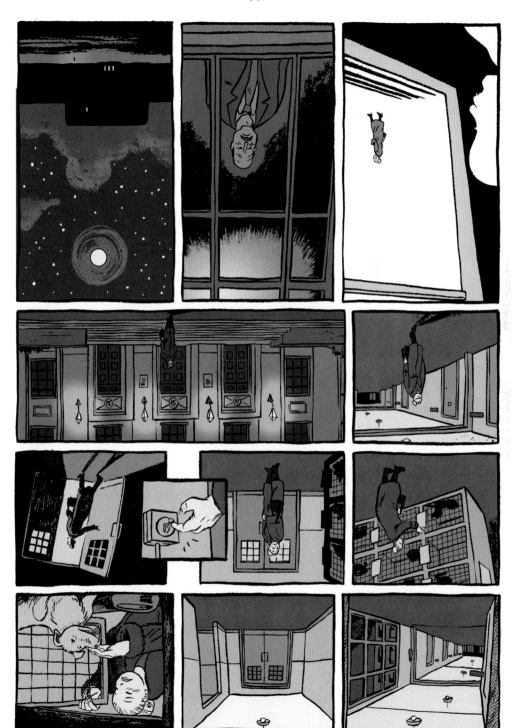

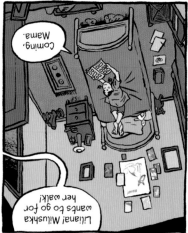

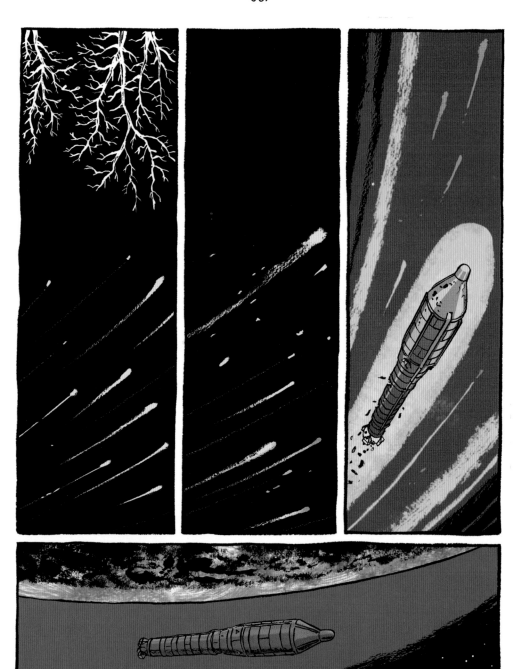

April 13th,
1958

"Work with animals
is a source of suffering to all of us.
We treat them like babies who cannot speak.
The more time passes,
the more I'm sorry about it.
We did not learn enough from the mission
to justify the death of the dog."

Oleg Georgivitch Gazenko, 1998

afterword

THE SOVIET UNION stunned the world with the launch of *Sputnik 1*, the world's first artificial satellite, on October 4, 1957. Coming at the height of the Cold War, this bold statement of the country's technological prowess was a momentous move in the global chess game against the US – which would culminate exactly five years later with the Cuban missile crisis, that brought the world closer to nuclear war than ever before or since.

It is very hard today to imagine the atmosphere of these times. How could Nikita Khrushchev, the Soviet premier, decide that this dazzling success had to be followed up with yet another, in time for the 40th anniversary of the October Revolution (November 7, by the Western calendar)? That one-month timing was far too short, even for the brilliant minds running the USSR's space program, and it sealed Laika's fate by making her mission a one-way trip.

As the quote from Oleg Gazenko at the end of the book shows, the scientific value of *Sputnik 2* was minimal; it contributed little to the first manned space flight by Yuri Gagarin in April 1961. Even the propaganda hit was marred by an outcry over Laika having been sent to die in space. The official story at the time was that she had survived four days in orbit, when in fact stress and overheating in the capsule had killed her in less than five hours.

Nick Abadzis researched with impressive thoroughness—from the stacks of the British Library to Korolev's house in Moscow—all the facts that have come to light since the collapse of the Soviet Union. He then wove all available historical elements into an unforgettable narrative that achieves the power of myth. Cutting through the official deceit spread at the time, the story brings out the truly heroic dedication that these exceptional scientists showed, even as they lived in a climate of suspicion and fear. And Nick's imagination seamlessly filled out the personal stories, both canine and human, that bring Laika alive as a meditation on the meaning of destiny and the fragile beauty of trust.

– Alexis Siegel, 2007

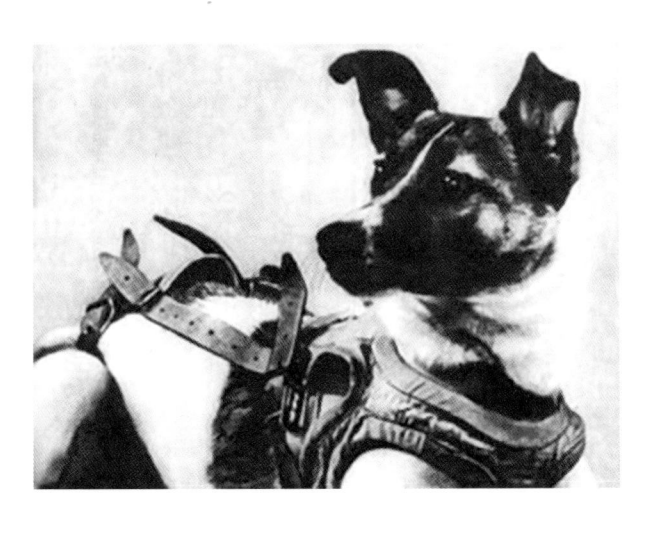

BIBLIOGRAPHY

Books

Applebaum, Anne. *Gulag: A History.* 2003.

Békési, Lázló, and Török, György. *Soviet Uniforms and Militaria 1917 – 1991 in Colour Photographs.* 2000.

Dickson, Paul. *Sputnik—the Shock of the Century.* 2001.

Dubbs, Chris. *Space Dogs—Pioneers of Space Travel.* 2003.

Feifer, George. *The Red Files—Secrets from the Russian Archives.* 2000.

Golovanov, Yaroslav. *Korolev: Fakty i Mify* (in Russian). 1994

Harford, James. *Korolev: How One Man Masterminded the Soviet Drive to Beat America to the Moon.* 1997.

Semenov, Yuri P. *Rocket and Space Corporation Energia—the Legacy of S. P. Korolev.* Robert Godwin, ed., English edition. 2001.

Siddiqi, Asif. *Sputnik and the Soviet Space Challenge.* 2000.

Solomko, Y., ed. Memorial Museum of Cosmonautics brochure. N.d.

Video

Smithsonian Videohistory Program. *Soviet Space Medicine.* Interviews with Oleg Gazenko, Evgenii Shepelev, and Abraham Genin about their participation in the Soviet aviation and space medicine program. Interviews by Cathleen S. Lewis, translated by Andreas Tarnberg. (RU 95521). 1989.

Internet Sources

AllRefer.com: Soviet Union
http://reference.allrefer.com/country-guide-study/soviet-union/

Grahn, Sven. *Sputnik 2—More News from Distant History*
http://www.svengrahn.pp.se/histind/Sputnik2/sputnik2more.html

------. *Sputnik 2—Was It Really Built in Less then a Month?*
http://www.svengrahn.pp.se/histind/Sputnik2/Sputnik2.htm

Jorden, William J. "Soviet Fires Earth Satellite into Space?" *New York Times,* October 5, 1957.
http://www.nytimes.com/partners/aol/special/sputnik/sput-01.html

Korolev, Sergei P. *Synopsis of Report on Development of Conceptual Design of an Artificial Earth Satellite.* (Technical Plan for Object D Satellite for U.S.S.R. Government Officials). 1956
http://www.hq.nasa.gov/office/pao/History/sputnik/russ3.html

LePage, Andrew J. *Sputnik 2: The First Animal in Orbit.*
http://www.seds.org/spaceviews/9711/index.html

NASA. *Sputnik 2.*
http://nssdc.gsfc.nasa.gov/nmc/tmp/1957-002A.html

Siddiqi, Asif. *Korolev, Sputnik, and the International Geophysical Year.*
http://inventors.about.com

S. P. Korolev Rocket and Space Corporation Energia.
http://www.energia.ru/English/

The Story of Laika.
http://www.moscowanimals.org/laika.html

Zak, Anatoly. *RussianSpaceWeb.com*
http://www.russianspaceweb.com/index.html

AUTHOR'S NOTE:

In this book, all phases of the moon depicted on specific dates are accurate to the day—although I may have erred on the side of drama about the time of moonrises. So thanks to Paul Carlisle for his very useful online "Moon Phases Calendar." http://www.paulcarlisle.net.old/MoonCalendar.html

For Pierre Alexander Abadzis

1925 - 2003

Acknowledgements

Thank You

For assistance and advice in technical and research matters:

Kelly Crawford, Mykola Krasnokutsky, Al Muell, Katya Rogatchevskaia, Asif Siddiqi, Dave Sutton, Charles P. Vick and Anatoly Zak.

For all the support, help and inspiration:

Jessica Abel, The Aggs Family, Greg Bennett, Nick Bertozzi, The Bentley Family, Alan Cowsill, Gina Gagliano, Siobhan Gallagher, Rob Green, Myla Goldberg, Kat Kopit, Jason Little, Matt Madden, Steve Marchant, Tanya McKinnon, Danica Novgorodoff, Charlie Orr, Paul Peart-Smith, Juliet Penney, Chris Pitzer, Masha Rudina, Caspar Sewell, Mark Siegel, Xenia Sinclair-Murray, Hilary Sycamore, John West, Sally Willis and all my wonderful friends at Eaglemoss.

Special thanks to Jim Green and the Abadzis Family (especially Angela and Nadia).

If I've forgotten anyone, my apologies and please write your name in here:

Mention and thanks must also be made to (living composers only): John Barry, Brian Eno, Neil Hannon, Joe Hisaishi, Bear McCreary and Thomas Newman, to whose music much of this book was drawn.

Please visit:

www.nickabadzis.com

http://www.moscowanimals.org

http://www.russianspaceweb.com

http://www.jimbus.co.uk/

First Second

New York & London

Copyright © 2007 by Nick Abadzis

Published by First Second
First Second is an imprint of Roaring Brook Press,
a division of Holtzbrinck Publishing Holdings Limited Partnership
175 Fifth Avenue, New York, NY 10010

Distributed in Canada by H. B. Fenn and Company Ltd.
Distributed in the United Kingdom by Macmillan Children's Books,
a division of Pan Macmillan.

Design by Danica Novgorodoff and Charles Orr
Laika photograph from the author's private collection

Cataloging-in-Publication Data is on file at the Library of Congress.

ISBN: 978-1-59643-702-9

First Second books are available for special promotions and premiums.
For details, contact: Director of Special Markets, Holtzbrinck Publishers.

First Edition September 2007

Printed in June 2010 in China by South China Printing Co. Ltd.,
Dongguan City, Guangdong Province

1 3 5 7 9 10 8 6 4 2